SONGBOOK FOR THE TROOPS

Songbook for the Troops

GLORIE
MUSIC

KINGSWAY MUSIC
EASTBOURNE

ISBN 0 86065 833 3

Cover photographs by David Thatcher

Cover design by Ron Bryant-Funnell

Printed in Great Britain for
KINGSWAY MUSIC LTD
1, St Anne's Road, Eastbourne, E. Sussex BN21 3UN
Stanley L. Hunt (Printers) Ltd, Rushden, Northants.

INDEX

Titles where different from first lines are shown in *italics*

1. AS THE FIERY SUN SHINES BRIGHT
(A promise from Your lips)

Ishmael

With feeling

Verse

1. As the fier-y sun shines bright, Your love is warmth in - side _ me,

as the crash-ing wave strikes shore, You re-mind me of Your power;

as a mo-ther feeds her young, You nur-ture and sus - tain ___ me,

in my Fa-ther's lov - ing arms, I know I am se - cure.

Chorus

And there's no - thing in this world could come be - tween _ us,

hell it - self will try, but it will not pre - vail;

for You will ne - ver leave _ me in this world to fight a -

lone and a pro-mise from Your lips can ne - ver fail. _____

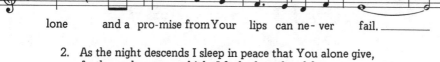

2. As the night descends I sleep in peace that You alone give,
As the eagle soars on high, I feel released and free;
As the wind blows wild and strong, my faith remains unshaken,
As a little baby cries, my every tear You see.

2. BEGONE YOU EVIL–MINDED MEN
(Psalm 119:115)

Ishmael

Be-gone,— you ev - il mind-ed men, don't

try to stop me from o - bey-ing God's com - mands. Be-gone,

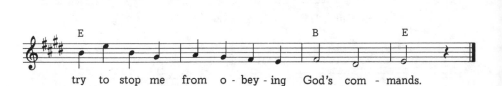

— you ev - il mind - ed men, don't

try to stop me from o - bey - ing God's com - mands.

3.
COME ON
(Let's praise the Lord)

Come on _ and let's praise the Lord, come on _ and let's praise the

Lord, come on _ and let's praise the Lord to - geth -

er.   Come on __ and let's   Lord.   with   our

hands in the   air, __ and our   feet off the ground, let's tell ev-'ry-bo-dy of the

joy that we've found. With our hands in the   air, __ and our   feet off the ground, let's

tell ev-'ry-bo-dy of the   joy that we've found. With our hands in the air, __ and our

feet off the ground, let's   tell   ev-'ry-bo-dy of the   joy that we've found.   In

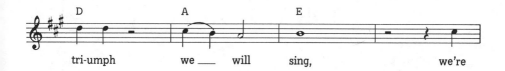

tri-umph   we __ will   sing,   we're

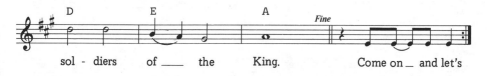

sol - diers   of __ the   King.   Come on __ and let's

2. We will shout, clap hands, and keep dancing around,
    Let's tell everybody of the joy that we've found.   *x3*
    In triumph we will sing,
    We're soldiers of the King.

4. DEAR LORD, MY FATHER
(The Lord's prayer)

Ishmael

With feeling

1. Dear Lord, my Fa-ther who's in heav'n, hon-oured be ___ Your ho-ly name; ___ may Your king-dom come, may Your will be done ___ here on earth ___ as it is ___ in heav'n. A - men, a - men, a - men, a - men. A - men.

1st time

2nd time

2. Dear Lord, please give us food today,
   And forgive us, as we forgive others.
   May Your testing be not too hard to bear,
   And deliver us from the evil one.

5. DON'T BE LAZY

Ishmael
Heb 6:12

With pace

Don't be la - zy, la - zy, la - zy, la - zy, but co - py those who through faith and pat-ience re - ceive what God has prom - ised.

6.

DON'T LOOK BACK
(Training up the troops)

Lively

Ishmael

1. Don't look back, — we must look for-ward. To whom will we pass — our ba-ton on? — A — life of ex - per - ience, — but with whom have we shared it? Who will suc - ceed us when we have all gone? —

Chorus
Train ing up the troops, train - ing up the troops, our life's work is train - ing up the troops. Mak - ing new re-cruits, then train - ing new re-cruits, our life's work is train - ing up the troops.

2. We

2. We may have excelled in our God-given gifting,
   But what is one person in a world of this size?
   Little soldiers need to be apprenticed by someone,
   To gain expertise they need to learn from the wise.

3. To train others is essential for the growth of the kingdom,
   Teach as you preach—should be our maxim.
   Then as young ones develop, teacher's greatest achievement
   Is that his trainees have now proved more successful than him.

7. DOWN IN A NOISY SMALL VALLEY
[The Glories]

Capo 4(C)

Ishmael/Dave Evans

Cheerfully

1. Down in a noi - sy small vall - ey, _____ some-where near Char - is - mat - ic Wood, _____ lived a litt - le _____ band _ of Glo - ries _____ who sang _ as loud as they could. _____

Chorus

Al - le - lu - ia, al - le, al - le - lu - ia, al - le, al - le - lu - ia, a - men. _____

Al - le - lu - ia, al - le, al - le - lu - ia, al - le, al - le - lu - ia, a - men. _____

2. Their vocabulary wasn't enormous,
   In fact it was really quite small.
   If it wasn't worth saying 'Alleluia'
   It wasn't worth saying at all.

3. Instead of legs they had bed springs,
   Which helped them keep jumping around,
   And with tambourine at the ready
   This is how they look and sound:

CHORUS

4. But these little folks always were happy,
   A grin reached from ear to ear.
   They always found lots to thank God for,
   And never had nothing to fear.

5. The Glories though had opposition,
   The Miseries were the name of their foes.
   They hated to see Glories dancing,
   And this song got right up their nose:

CHORUS

6. Well the Miseries decided to take action,
   Whilst the Glories were sleeping they'd nip
   Up to them and dislocate their bed-springs,
   And with a needle they'd sew up their lip.

7. But as they crept into the Glorie camp,
   They panicked and in seconds were gone,
   'Cause all the sleeping little Glories
   Were merrily snoring this song:

CHORUS

8. Well this song of course has a meaning,
   And this is the point of the story:
   Life on this earth can be misery,
   Or life on this earth can be glory.

CHORUS

8. FATHER GOD, I WONDER

Ishmael

Sensitively, crescendo on chorus

Fa-ther God, I won-der how I __ man-aged to ex-ist with-out the

know-ledge of Your par-ent-hood, __ and Your lov-ing __ care. But

now I am Your son, I am a-dop-ted in Your fam-il-y, and

I can ne-ver be a-lone, 'cause Fa-ther God, You're there be-side me.

I will sing Your prai-ses, I will sing Your prai-ses, I will

1st time

sing Your prai-ses for e-ver - more.

2nd time

for e-ver - more.

9. 5000+ HUNGRY FOLK

Ishmael

Happily

1. 5 0 0 0 + hun-gry folk.＿ 5 0 0 0 + hun-gry' folk. ＿ 5

1st, 2nd & 3rd times

0 0 0 + hun-gry folk came＿ 4 2 list-en 2 Je - sus.

Last time

1 2 3 4 5 6 7 8 9 10 11 12 bas-kets-ful left o - ver.

2. The 6 x 2 said 000,
   The 6 x 2 said 000,
   The 6 x 2 said 000,
   Where can 1 get some food from?

3. Just 1 had 1 2 3 4 5,
   Just 1 had 1 2 3 4 5,
   Just 1 had 1 2 3 4 5,
   Loaves and 1 2 fishes.

4. When Jesus blessed the 5 + 2,
   When Jesus blessed the 5 + 2,
   When Jesus blessed the 5 + 2,
   They were increased many x over.

5. 5000 + 8 it up,
   5000 + 8 it up,
   5000 + 8 it up,
   With 1 2 3 4 5 6 7 8 9 10 11 12 basketsful left over.

10. GLORIE

Ishmael

Getting faster

G L O R I E, U R 1 2 I C. Glo-rie, Glo-ries ev-'ry-where, if

not there soon will be. G L O R I E, we're a mas-sive fa-mi - ly, and it's

Je - sus, you and me make up the Glo - rie Com - pa - ny.

G L O

11. GLORIE ELECTRO−REEL

As a 'jig'

12. GOD IS HERE, GOD IS HERE
(Almighty God is here)

Ishmael

2. As I see my generation in sadness and in pain,
   I hear the fools say there's no God, time and time again,
   But fools can never change the fact our King is here to reign,
   Almighty God is here.

3. So let's call together all the saints, their voices to proclaim
   That the Father, Son and Spirit will forever be the same,
   And the day will come when every knee shall bow at Jesus' name,
   Almighty God is here.

13. GOD IS HERE, GOD IS PRESENT

Ishmael
Mt 5:3-10

With feeling

God is — here, God is — pres-ent, — God is mov-ing by His

Spi - rit, — can you hear what He is say-ing, — are you will-ing to re-

spond? God is — here, God is — pres-ent, — God is mov-ing by His

Spi-rit, — Lord I o-pen up my life to You, | please do just what You

1st time
want. God is — want.

2nd time
Lord I — won't stop

lov - ing You, — You mean more to me — than

an - y - thing else. — Lord I — won't stop lov - ing You,

— You mean more to me — than life — it -self. —

14. HEAVENLY FATHER
(Children of God's family)

Ishmael

Hea - ven - ly Fa - ther, we would sing out Your praise,

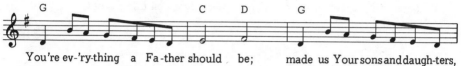

You're ev - 'ry - thing a Fa - ther should be; made us Your sons and daugh - ters,

made us Your own, child - ren of God's fa - mi - ly. 1. We

old - er ones say, 'young - er ones, we'll love and care for you;' we

young ones say to old - er ones 'our love res - pects you too.'__ We love You.

2. Father, as a family
We will live forever;
Your Church is made of all ages
Who love to be together.
We love You.

15. HE ARRIVED IN THE TOWN
(The Marksman)

Ishmael/D. Evans

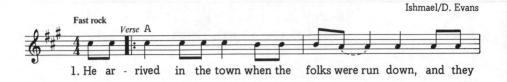

1. He ar - rived in the town when the folks were run down, and they

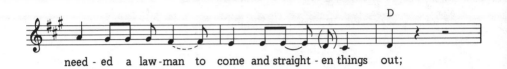

need - ed a law-man to come and straight - en things out;

but the crowd were hop - ing for a guy who'd be tot - ing a

Colt for - ty -five, _ or car-ried a Sten _ gun a - bout. ____

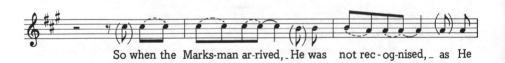

So when the Marks-man ar-rived, _ He was not rec - og-nised, _ as He

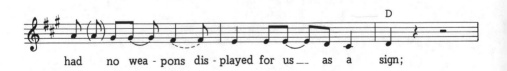

had no wea - pons dis - played for us __ as a sign;

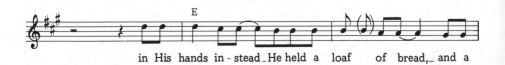

in His hands in - stead _ He held a loaf of bread, _ and a

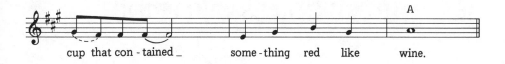

cup that con-tained _ some-thing red like wine.

Chorus   F#m

His life's an ac - tion re play, He
(ac - tion) (re - play)

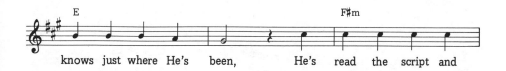

E   F#m

knows just where He's been, He's read the script and

E

learned His lines and shot the fi - nal scene,

D   E   *Fine*

and shot the fi - nal scene. (2.) They

2. They laughed at His style for a little while,
   But in time they felt the power of the things He taught.
   It was like a dart, shooting into man's heart,
   Then He'd revive the victim with the bread and the wine that He'd bought.
   Well some would cheer, but most would fear,
   The pointed directness of the Marksman's aim.
   And though some admired, the majority were tired of the side effects
   Of the stranger's claim.

3. Hey, people grew sick of what they thought was a trick,
   And said it's time to show this guy just who's right.
   So armed to the teeth they dragged Him into the street,
   And said 'Marksman, now's the time to prove you can fight.'
   And as their bullets struck home the Marksman groaned,
   'Father forgive them' is what He said;
   Then as He dies, before our very eyes, His body disappeared,
   And just left the wine and bread.

16. HERE COMES THE BRIDE

Ishmael

17. I DON'T NEED TO BE BIG TO BE BEAUTIFUL

Ishmael

I don't need to be big _ to be beau - ti - ful, I don't

need some great big mus-cles to be strong. I don't need sil-ver hair nor

loads of clothes to wear to be as wise as might - y So - lo -

mon, bom bom. I just need to be a spe - cial friend of

Je - sus, and do all the things that He wants me to

do, then I'll be beau - ti - ful and strong, I'll live for

right and not for wrong, and be a hap - pi - er and wi - ser per - son

To repeat / *Last time*

too, oo, oo, oo, I I I I don't too.

18. I LOVE THE LIGHT OF DAYTIME
(Little troopers)

Ishmael

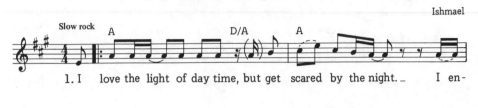

Slow rock

1. I love the light of day time, but get scared by the night.＿ I en-

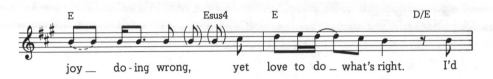

joy ＿ do-ing wrong, yet love to do ＿ what's right. I'd

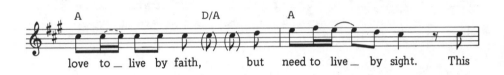

love to ＿ live by faith, but need to live ＿ by sight. This

1st & 2nd times / *3rd time*

sol-dier's got a lot to learn.＿ 2./3. I'd ＿ but who's going to

4th time

teach me? 4. Al - ＿ 5. I'm fed

5th time

＿ this sol-dier's got a lot to learn, ＿ this

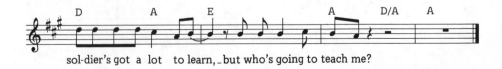

sol-dier's got a lot to learn,＿but who's going to teach me?

2. I'd love to enjoy giving — but I'd much rather receive.
   I'd love to possess wisdom — but I'm totally naive.
   I'd love to be Spirit-filled — but I just cannot believe.
   This soldier's got a lot to learn.

3. I'd love to know the Bible — but I find it hard to read.
   I'd love to pray much more — but I do not see the need.
   Spiritually I'm starving but I don't know how to feed.
   This soldier's got a lot to learn,
   But who's going to teach me?

4. Although I may be gifted — my character is poor.
   Although I may be saved — I don't understand what for.
   I'm exhausted, needing help — and just cannot go on much more.
   This soldier's got a lot to learn.

5. I'm fed up with silly stories — and modelling plasticine,
   And being told I'm too young to talk — in church be even seen.
   Though I'm just a child — I'm still a spiritual being.
   This soldier's got a lot to learn.
   This soldier's got a lot to learn.
   This soldier's got a lot to learn,
   But who's going to teach me?

19. I'M A LITTLE GLORIE

Ishmael

Rock 'n' roll

1. I'm a lit - tle Glo - rie and I'm in the best team,

I'm a lit - tle Glo - rie and I'm in the best team,

I'm a lit - tle Glo - rie and I'm in the best team,

I'm a lit - tle Glo - rie and I'm in the best team,

I'm a lit - tle Glo - rie, I'm a lit - tle Glo - rie,

To repeat

I'm a lit - tle Glo - rie.

I'm a lit - tle Glo - rie and I'm in the Lord's team.

2. I'm a little Glorie and I'm in the Lord's team . . .

20. I WANT TO LEARN ABOUT JESUS

Ishmael

With swing

1. I want to learn a - bout Je - sus, __ I want to

learn a - bout Je - sus, __ I want to

learn a - bout Je - sus, __ I

on - ly want to learn a - bout, I on - ly want to learn a - bout, I

on - ly want to learn a - bout Je - sus. __

2. I want to talk about . . .

3. I want to sing about . . .

4. I want to shout about . . .

21. I WILL CALL UPON THE LORD

Ishmael

Ps 55:16, 17

La la la la la la la la la la la la la la la la la la la la la la la la la la la la la la la. La la la. I will call u-pon the Lord, ask-ing Him to save me, and He will, yes He will, yes He will. I pray morn-ing, noon and night, plead-ing loud-ly with my God, and He will hear and He will ans - wer all my prayers.

22. I WILL CLICK MY FINGERS

Ishmael

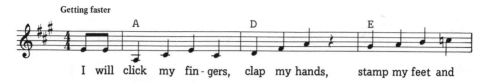

I will click my fin-gers, clap my hands, stamp my feet and

shout ha - le-lu - jah! Then I'll whistle as loud as I can: (whistle)

I'm hap-py I'm a child of the Lord. ___

23. LORD, I WANT TO BE A GLORIE

Ishmael

Lord, I want to be Glo - rie. Lord, You know I real - ly

do. I re - a - lise that You want all of me, ___ and

Lord, I just want You ___ to - night, I just want You.

24. LIGHT A FLAME

Mick Gisbey

With energy

Light a flame with in my heart that's burn - ing bright;

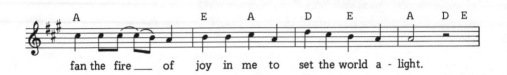

fan the fire ___ of joy in me to set the world a - light.

Let my flame be - gin to spread, my life to glow;

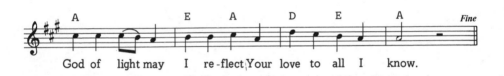

God of light may I re-flect Your love to all I know.

Verse

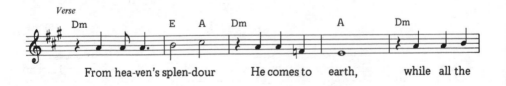

From hea-ven's splen-dour He comes to earth, while all the

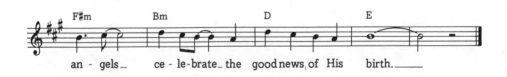

an - gels ___ ce - le-brate ___ the good news of His birth. ___

2. We too exalt You,
   Our glorious King;
   Jesus our Saviour
   Paid the price to take away our sin.

25. LORD I STRIVE

Ishmael

1. Lord I strive, but so oft-en fail, want to win_but can't seem to suc-ceed; please pour out Your mer-cy _ on _ me. _____ I try to do Your_ will, but there's so much to _ ful-fill, as I take my eyes off me I see Your glo-ry. _____

I see Your _ glo-ry, _ God of grace, God of glo-ry; _ I see _ Your _ glo-ry, _ God of grace, God of glo-ry to me. _____ God of glo-ry to me. _____

2. Lord I have such little faith,
I'm silent when I know I should speak,
Please pour out Your mercy on me.
I should be bold but I just feel fear,
When You talk I don't seem to hear,
But as I take my eyes off me
I see Your glory.

3. Lord at times I am not real,
Hold back when I know I should give,
Please pour out Your mercy on me.
When tempted I sometimes fall,
Am I any use at all?
But as I take my eyes off me
I see Your glory.

26. LORD, I NEED TO KNOW YOU LOVE ME

Ishmael

With feeling

Lord, I need to know You love me,
Lord, I need to know You love me,

Lord, I need to know You care;
Lord, I need to be as-sured;

in those times I feel re-
in those times I feel re-

ject-ed, I need to know You there.
ject-ed, that You still love me, Lord.

God says, 'List-en, My litt-le child,

I'm a Fath-er who'll nev-er leave you,

and though all your friends may fail you,

You can al-ways trust in Me.

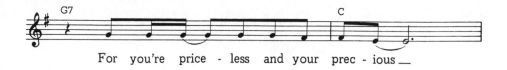

For you're price - less and your prec - ious ___

and your val - ue can - not be meas - ured, ___

you're an heir ___ to My king - dom, ___

you're in My chos - en fam - i - ly.' _____

27. LORD, YOU GAVE ME JOY IN MY HEART

Ishmael

Happily, with actions

Lord, You gave _ me joy _ in my heart, joy _ in my heart al-ways, and it's You I want to _ praise.

Lord, You gave _ me peace in my mind, peace in my mind al-ways; _ peace _ in my mind, joy _ in my heart, and it's You I want to _ praise.

Lord, You gave _ me _ a song in my mouth, a song in my mouth al-ways; ____ a song in my mouth, peace _ in my mind, joy _ in my heart, and it's You I want to _ praise.

Lord, You gave me hands that will clap, hands that will clap al-ways; _ hands.

that will clap, a song in my mouth, peace _ in my mind, joy _

_ in my heart, and it's You I want to _ praise.

Lord, You gave _ me feet _ that can dance, feet _ that can dance al -

ways; ____ feet _ that can dance, hands _ that will clap, a

song in my mouth, peace _ in my mind, joy _ in my heart, and it's

You I want to _ praise. Lord, You gave _ me _ a love for o - thers, _ a

love for o - thers al - ways; ____ a love for o - thers, _ feet _

_ that can dance, hands _ that will clap, a song in my mouth, peace _

_ in my mind, joy _ in my heart, and it's You I want to _ praise.

28. LORD, WE'VE COME TO WORSHIP YOU

Ishmael

With a gentle rhythm

Lord, we've come_ to wor-ship You._ Lord, we've come to praise. Lord we've come_ to wor-ship You,_ in oh, so man-y ways._ Some of us shout and some of us sing, and some of us whis-per the praise we bring, but Lord, we all___ are ga-ther-ing___ to give to You_ our praise.

29. MARCHING ORDERS

Ishmael

In a marching style

30. MISSION ACCOMPLISHED

Ishmael

Steadily

31. MAY THE PEACE AND PRESENCE OF THE LORD

Ishmael/Andy Piercy

Gently, but flowing

May the peace and pres - ence of the Lord —

fill our — hearts and minds to o - ver - flow - ing, —

to keep our rad - i - ance show - ing, — keep our love for You

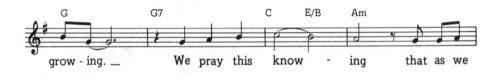

grow - ing. — We pray this know - ing that as we

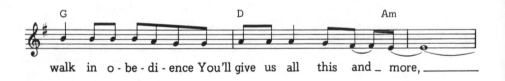

walk in o - be - di - ence You'll give us all this and — more, _____

— that as we walk in o - be - di - ence You'll give us all this and — more.

_____ My Lord _____ my God, _____ the

first - born   of   cre - a - tion, ___ the   au - thor ___

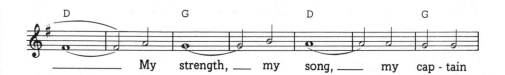

___ and per - fec - ter   of   my   faith. _____

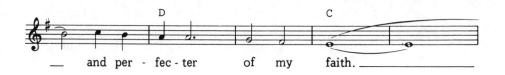

_____ My   strength, ___ my   song, ___ my   cap - tain

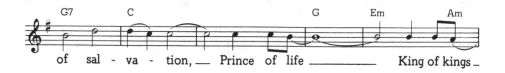

of   sal - va - tion, ___ Prince of life _____ King of kings _

___ God   of   grace. _____

32. NICODEMUS

Quick reggae rhythm

1. 'Ni-co - de - mus, what's_ this you say, you want to know the truth?
come, now, learn-ed teach-er, your in - struc-tions leave me cold;

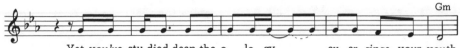

Yet you've stu-died deep the-o - lo - gy_____ ev - er since your youth.
how can I be like a new-born babe_whilst I am grow - ing old?

You've_ tried to ex-pand your mind so much with_ truth that's turned to
D'you ex-pect me to think that I could shrink and re-turn in - to a

lies, if you be - came like a new born babe,_ you'd____
womb? There's more dis-tance be tween my_ cradle and I _____ than there

1st time

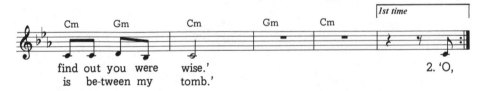

find out you were wise.' 2. 'O,
is be-tween my tomb.'

2nd time

3. 'Ni-co - de-mus,_ I'm talk-ing a-bout your spi-rit and not the shell it's
- de-mus dis-ap-peared _ in - to the night, the same way as he

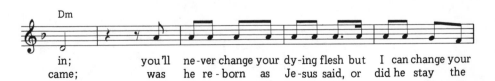

in; you'll ne-ver change your dy-ing flesh but I can change your
came; was he re - born as Je-sus said, or did he stay the

33. NOW I'VE GROWN OLDER
(Little troopers revisited)

Ishmael

Quickly

A
1. Now I've grown old-er, — I'm now in my mid-teens, my

E
church has taught me well, — through ma-ny ways and means; — but

A
still it seems to please them if I stay be-hind the scenes, I've

D   A   E | 1st, 2nd & 4th times | | 3rd time |
still got a lot — to give. — 2. I've been — I've

D   A   E   A
still got a lot — to give, — but who's gon-na trust — me?

| 5th time |
3. You — I've

D   A   E   D   A   E
still got a lot — to give, — this sol-dier's got a lot to give,

A   Fine
— but who's gon-na trust — me? —

2. I've been taught to study Scripture if I really want to grow,
   I've found the more I've read in depth, the more I want to know;
   But when I'm full of Bible, then where am I to go?
   I've still got a lot to give . . .

3. I'm told I've got a ministry, one of the chosen few,
   I'm told there is a task in life that only I can do;
   But why can't I begin it 'fore my teenage years are through?
   I've still got a lot to give, I've still got a lot to give . . .
   But who's gonna trust me?

4. You saw me as a child, now see me as I am.
   I'm wanting to be used by God, in every way I can;
   But please will you include me in the strategy you plan?
   I've still got a lot to give . . .

5. Leaders, will you listen as I bring to you my plea.
   Let me learn to cope with some responsibility;
   Has the church that you are building got any room for me?
   I've still got a lot to give, I've still got a lot to give.
   This soldier's got a lot to give . . .but who's gonna trust me?

34. SO IF YOU THINK YOU'RE STANDING FIRM

Capo 4 (C)

Ishmael
1 Cor 10:12

So if you think you're stand-ing firm be care-ful you don't fall, so if you think you're stand-ing firm be care-ful you don't fall, so if you think you're stand-ing firm be care-ful you don't fall, so if you think you're stand-ing firm be care-ful you don't fall.

35. SO WE'RE MARCHING ALONG
(The Lord's army)

Ishmael

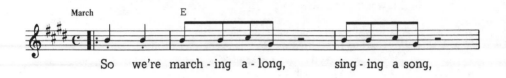

So we're march-ing a-long, sing-ing a song,

we're in the Lord's ar - my. We're fight-ing for right as we're

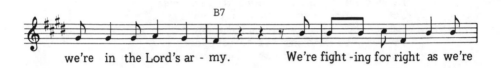

learn-ing what's wrong, 'cause _ we're in the Lord's ar - my.

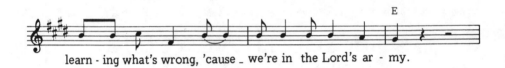

He's got the vic-tory, so let's real-ly shout, we're in the Lord's ar-

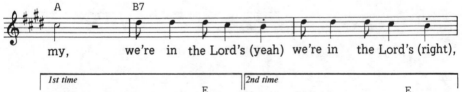

my, we're in the Lord's (yeah) we're in the Lord's (right),

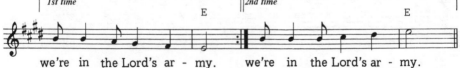

1st time   *2nd time*

we're in the Lord's ar - my.   we're in the Lord's ar - my.

36. SO JOIN THE ROYAL PRAYER FORCE
(The royal prayer force)

Ishmael

37. THE BATTLE'S TOUGH
(The deserter)

Ishmael

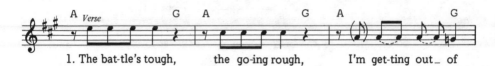

1. The bat-tle's tough, the go-ing rough, I'm get-ting out _ of

here. I see no hope, I can not cope,

I'm in the wrong _ ca - reer. But as I walk from the front _ line,

I hear a gen-tle voice say: _ 'To de-sert _ will bring dan-

- ger, You'll be saved _ if you stay.' ___

2. Think I know best — more than the rest,
   Is this what life's all about?
   It's not my battle — it's not my war,
   I signed up but want out.

3. In civvy street — life's incomplete,
   No peace, only pain.
   Security awaits for me
   Back on the front line again.

   So I return to the front line,
   I hear a gentle voice say:
   'To desert will bring danger,
   You'll be saved if you stay.'

38. THE COMMISSION

Ishmael

39. THERE'S NOTHING BETTER

Ishmael

Strongly

There's no-thing bet - ter than be-ing a sol-dier in the ar-my of the Lord. There's no-thing bet-ter than be-ing a sol - dier in the ar-my of the Lord. We'll live by faith and not by sight, not by pow-er, not by might, but by His Spi-rit win ev-'ry fight.

40.

3 9 THIRTY—NINE

Ishmael

Steadily

Verse

1. 3 9 thir - ty - nine, thir - ty - nine books are in the Old Test - a-ment. 2 7 twen - ty se-ven, but there's on - ly twen - ty-se-ven in the New. But just one ho - ly God could bring a book to life and pro - mise ev - 'ry page is true. The one and on - ly

Last time to Coda ✛

liv - ing God told the wri-ters what they should and should-n't do.

✛ *CODA*

wri - ters what they should and should-n't do.

2. 2 8 twenty-eight,
Over twenty-eight authors in the Old Testament,
But just 9, only nine,
There are only nine authors in the New.

3. 2 , 0 0 0
Two thousand years are covered in the Old Testament,
But even less than 1 0 0
Less than a hundred years are covered in the New.

41. THERE WAS A LITTLE MAN
(Little man)

Ishmael

1. There was a lit-tle man, and he had a lit-tle house,

some-where near the gen-tle roll-ing sea. He found a lit-tle site that he

thought would suit him well, a per-fect place to build se-cu-ri-ty. Well, the

sand was le-vel,_ and the sand was flat,_ with a saw and a chi-sel,_ and a

rat-a-tat-tat; with a buck-et full of this,_ and a sho-vel full of that,_ his

house was ve-ry_ soon built. 'What a house,_ look,

come and see!'_ he said to all_ he knew;_ 'This

house will last_ as long as me!'_ And sad-ly that_ was true.

_ La la la _ la la   la la la, _   la la la la _ la la   la.

2. All was fine and rosy till the winter came along,
   Then suddenly the gentle rolling sea
   Became a little rough, and the winds began to blow,
   It began to smash his little property.
   For the winds went whoosh, and his house went splat,
   Just like a pancake it was flat.
   The wind and the rain had seen about that,
   There's now no house at all.
   'What a house, look, come and see!'
   His house has just spelt trouble;
   'This house will last as long as me!'
   Came a voice beneath the rubble.

3. Another little man built another little house
   Somewhere near the gentle rolling sea.
   He found a little site that he thought would suit him well,
   A perfect place to build security.
   Well, the rock was level, and the rock was flat,
   With a saw and a chisel and a rat-a-tat-tat;
   With a bucket full of this, and a shovel full of that,
   His house was very soon built.
   'What a house, look, come and see!
   I've built on a rock — it's stronger;
   This house will last as long as me,
   Forever, if not longer.'

4. All was fine and rosy till the winter came along,
   Then suddenly the gentle rolling sea
   Became a little rough, and the winds began to blow,
   But it couldn't harm his little property.
   For the winds went whoosh, but his house stood good,
   It stood as firm as a Christmas pud.
   The wind and the rains blew as hard as they could,
   But his house, it would not budge.
   'What a house, look, come and see!
   I've built on rock — it's stronger;
   This house will last as long as me,
   Forever, if not longer.'

42. WE ARE ALL ASSEMBLED

Mick Gisbey

1. We are all ass-em-bled _ be-fore the King of kings, as
He re-veals the batt-le we must face.
Ac-tive in the con-flict _ that He has o-ver-come, _ to-
geth-er be-ing taught_how'to fight, _ and live in vic-to-ry,
vic-to-ry march-ing on the con-quer-ing side;
vic-to-ry, vic-to-ry, Je-sus is our batt-le
cry. cry _____ our batt-le cry.

2. We are armed for battle,
Ready and alert,
Fighting in the army of our God;
Mastering the weapons
Forged by the King,
Trained to follow orders
We unite:

3. And soon the Prince of Peace will come,
And every eye will see
The great and shining glory of our God;
With songs of joyful triumph
Welcoming the King,
Forever giving glory unto Him:

43. WE ARE IN GOD'S ARMY

Capo 4 (C)

Ishmael

We are in God's ar-my we are in the ar-my of the Lord, yeah, yeah, yeah, we are in God's ar-my,

Glo-rie Glo-rie Glo-rie, the Glo-rie Com-pa-ny.

1. The en-em-y's at-tack-ing, con-vinced he's gain-ing ground, but the on-ly voice that he can hear is the one. He shouts a-round; but we're not fooled by his lies, we know that he is wrong, we may be weak as sol-diers but as an ar-my we are strong.

2. The enemy's regrouping, as he tries another plan,
   He can't pick off an army but he can pick out a man;
   So we'll stay close together, and sing this battle-song,
   We may be weak as soldiers but as an army we are strong.

3. The enemy's realising that his future's looking poor,
   Though he loves single combat, he's already lost the war;
   United not divided, together we belong,
   We may be weak as soldiers but as an army we are strong.

44. WE ARE THE GLORIE COMPANY

Ishmael

We are the Glo-rie Com-pa-ny, Com-pa-ny.

We are the Glo-rie Com-pa-ny.__ With Je-sus as our Sav-iour, we'll

live in vic-to-ry, 'cause we are the Glo-rie Com-pa-

ny, we you and me, we are the Glo-rie Com-pa-ny.

45. WE BELONG TO AN ARMY

Ishmael

1. We be-long_ to an ar-my that can nev-er be de-feat-ed;

we are part_ of a cause_ that can

nev-er nev-er fail; we are

fight - ing an ene -my who has pan - icked and re - treat ed;

and the gates of hell _ are

fall - ing, the _ gates of hell _ are fall - ing, ___ the

(3rd time rall.)

gates of hell are ___ fall - ing, ___ and God's

(3rd time D.S.)

king - dom will pre - vail. _____ 2. So we'll

2. So we'll sing a song of victory, we'll sing a song of joy;
   Praising in our spirits even death cannot destroy;
   Through Jesus we are winners, as kings we now proclaim;
   We are so much more than conquerors,
   We are so much more than conquerors,
   We are so much more than conquerors
   Through the power of Jesus' name.

3. So we're raising up our banners stating 'Jesus is victorious';
   Even though we're battle weary we'll endure to the end;
   Then King Jesus will return triumphant and victorious;
   There'll be no more wars and fighting,
   No more demonic battles,
   No more tears and pain.
   Because Satan's been destroyed.

   (Last time – slowly)
   There'll be peace and joy forever,
   There'll be love and life forever,
   We will praise His name forever,
   'Cause He's worthy to be praised.

46. WE WILL PRAISE YOU

Ishmael

With swing

Chorus

We will _ praise you, _____ we will _ praise You, _

_ we're for-ev-er _ grate-ful to our God and _

King. Your cross has _ freed us, _____ Your blood re -

leased us, _ from the in-flu-ence and the pow'r of

Fine *Verse*

sin. _____ 1. We've been blind to-wards the right, _ loved the

dark-ness, ha-ted the light; by our fool-ish-ness we've been

locked in chains and bound. _ But now these once blind eyes can see _

_ a Christ who gave His life for me, _ I'm no

Last time D.C. al Fine

lon-ger lost I am for-ev-er found. We will _

2. Though we've felt our hurts and fears,
   Though we've known those desert years,
   Though we've tasted hardship, pain and poverty;
   Though we've been cheated, hurt and used,
   Though we've been slandered and abused,
   Not one of these can match up to Calvary.

47. WHAT A LONG HARD DAY IT'S BEEN
(Angels)

Capo 1 (A)

Ishmael

1. What a long hard day it's been, you've had to take the rough with the smooth. These eyes are tired by what they've seen; it's not so ea-sy stand-ing up for truth. But forget the wars you've been in to-day, as no-thing can dis-turb you now, 'cause round your head are sta-tioned heaven's ar-mies. Just lay down wear-y child, lay down, lit-tle an-gel go to sleep, 'cause Fa-ther's here and He will keep you safe, 'cause Fa-ther's here and He will keep you safe.

2. What a long hard day it's been,
   At times you wondered if you'd make
   it through.
   Straight and narrow's tough and mean,
   As the pressure really gets to you.

3. What a long hard day it's been,
   To take His cross will mean you'll suffer
   pain.
   Though you're weak He'll keep you clean,
   Rest in Him and be renewed again.

48. YOU MAY THINK I'M SO YOUNG
(The grasshopper song)

Mick Gisbey

With life

Verse

You may think I'm so young, too young to un-der-stand; — don't for-get — in God's eyes He looks on me as grand. He ne-ver ne-ver li-mits — the Gi-ant that's in me; — He leads me through my child-hood su-per-nat-ural-ly. —

Chorus

I'm not a grass-hop-per, — I'm a Gi-ant in the Lord.

I'm not a grass-hop-per, — I'm a Gi-ant in the Lord. —

ISHMAEL

...the 'Troops' series...

TRAINING UP THE TROOPS
SFC180

This recording represents a significant stage in Ishmael's career, bringing his audience face to face with the facts of spiritual warfare, and the key to victory. A powerful album.

TRAINING UP THE TROOPS Vol 2
SFC194

The sequel – 15 great songs on a similar theme, including three instrumental tracks that will get you up on your feet.

TRAINING UP THE TROOPS 2 & THE BEST OF TRAINING UP THE TROOPS
Compact Disc SFCD195

A total of 70 minutes of pure, top-quality Ishmael on one compact disc – possibly the best value CD ever!

SONGS FOR LITTLE TROOPERS
SFC212

A special recording of Ish songs aimed at the under-8s. Containing a number of old favourites together with some brand-new material, the cassette also features backing tracks on Side Two. Amazing value for money.

Other Glorie Music recordings include:

RICH!
SFC203

Richard Hubbard is a man after Ishmael's own heart. 14 hi-energy tracks, including 'We will sing together', 'A band on ship' and the increasingly famous 'F.U.N.E.N.R.G?'

HOOKED ON ISHMAEL
SFC202

A dance pastiche of some of Ish's best-known songs, instrumentalised in the style of Stock/Aitken/Waterman by Tim Jupp, Ishmael's keyboard player.

LAND OF HOPE AND GLORIES/
THE POWER AND THE GLORIES
KMC479

Two of the best-loved Glorie albums on one cassette, Ishmael unashamedly confronts the themes of Christian character and spiritual gifts in a way that is accessible to children.

Order from your local Christian Bookshop, or in case of difficulty direct from:
The Rainbow Company, PO Box 77, Hailsham, E. Sussex BN27 3EF.

ISHMAEL'S CHILDREN'S PRAISE PARTY
Vol 1 & 2
SFC201

A double cassette of the first two of Ishmael's now famous praise party series, these recordings bounce along with teaching, praise and worship for the whole family.

ISHMAEL'S PRAISE PARTY Vol 3/
ISHMAEL'S SCRIPTURE PRAISE PARTY
SFC220

A new double cassette combining 23 praise party songs of non-stop energy, with 24 Bible verses set to music which enable you to learn Scripture by heart while having fun at the same time.

FAMILY PRAISE FAVOURITES
SFC144

Ishmael acknowledges that other people do write good songs as well as himself! He has collected on this album his favourite praise and worship songs and recorded them with his usual zest.
You will find that they're your favourites too!

ISHMAEL

... paperbacks ...

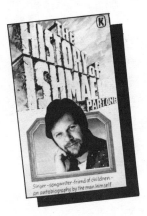

THE HISTORY OF ISHMAEL
Part One

Singer/songwriter, friend of children – the long-awaited autobiography.

272 pages including photos.

ANGELS WITH DIRTY FACES

Ishmael loves children – here's how and why!

CHILDREN OF THE VOICE

An enchanting tale for children of all ages, written in the spirit of *Pilgrim's Progess* and *Animal Farm*.

Order from your local Christian Bookshop, or in case of difficulty direct from:
The Rainbow Company, PO Box 77, Hailsham, E. Sussex BN27 3EF.